BABY ANIMALS

CHECKERBOARD PRESS ✦ NEW YORK

Goodness,
we're such tiny,
curious kittens.
Are those flowers,
or are they bells?
Let's find out.

These puppies
and kittens are pals,
you can see.
Is Kitty telling
her friend a secret?

Naughty Sandy
is chewing
his leash again.
It looks like fun!
One day, we'll be
grown-up
and won't get into
any more trouble.

AND when *we*
grow up,
we're going to be
big and strong
like our mothers!

Guinea pigs
and hamsters make
nice, fluffy pets.
But squirrels want
to stay in trees
and nibble acorns.

Baa-baa!
Oink-oink!
Moo-moo!

These baby animals
are enjoying
the spring
sunshine.

Hi, there,
little zebra,
giraffe, and llama.
We like to visit you
at the zoo —
and the cute baby
elephant, too!

Each animal
is different
and special. . . .
Fox is clever.
Penguin is wobbly.
Kangaroo is hoppity.
Baby Seal is cuddly.

What adorable
and playful cubs.
But watch out!
When they grow up,
they'll be as strong
as that big tiger.